Feeding Time

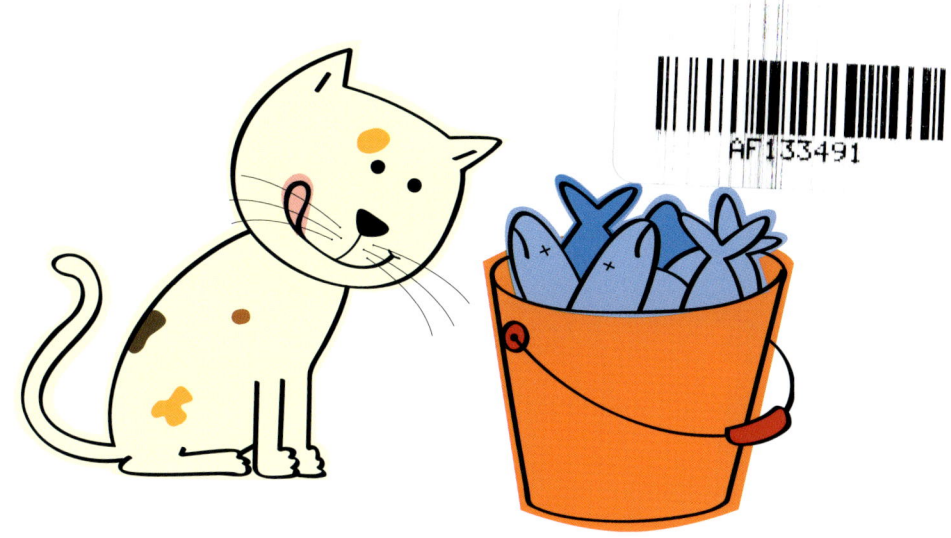

Maoliosa Kelly
Illustrated by Ian Cunliffe

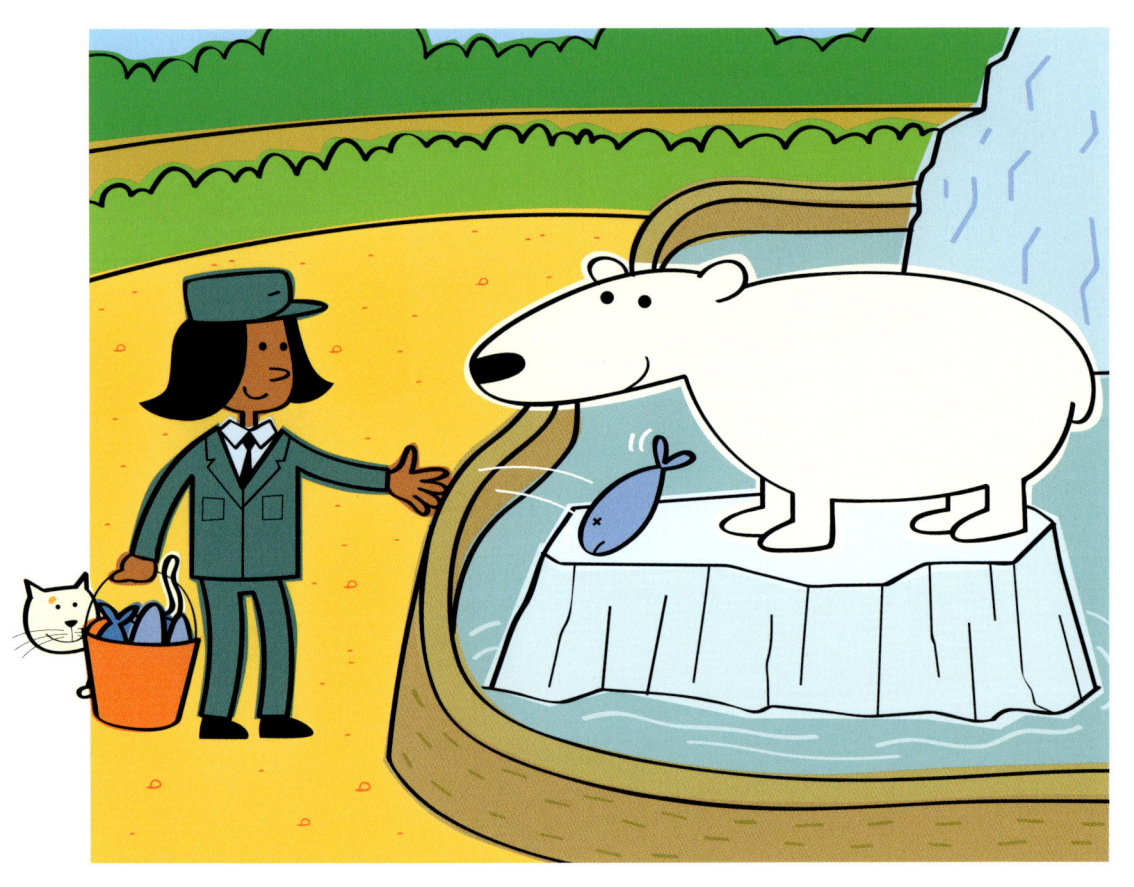

This is for the polar bear.

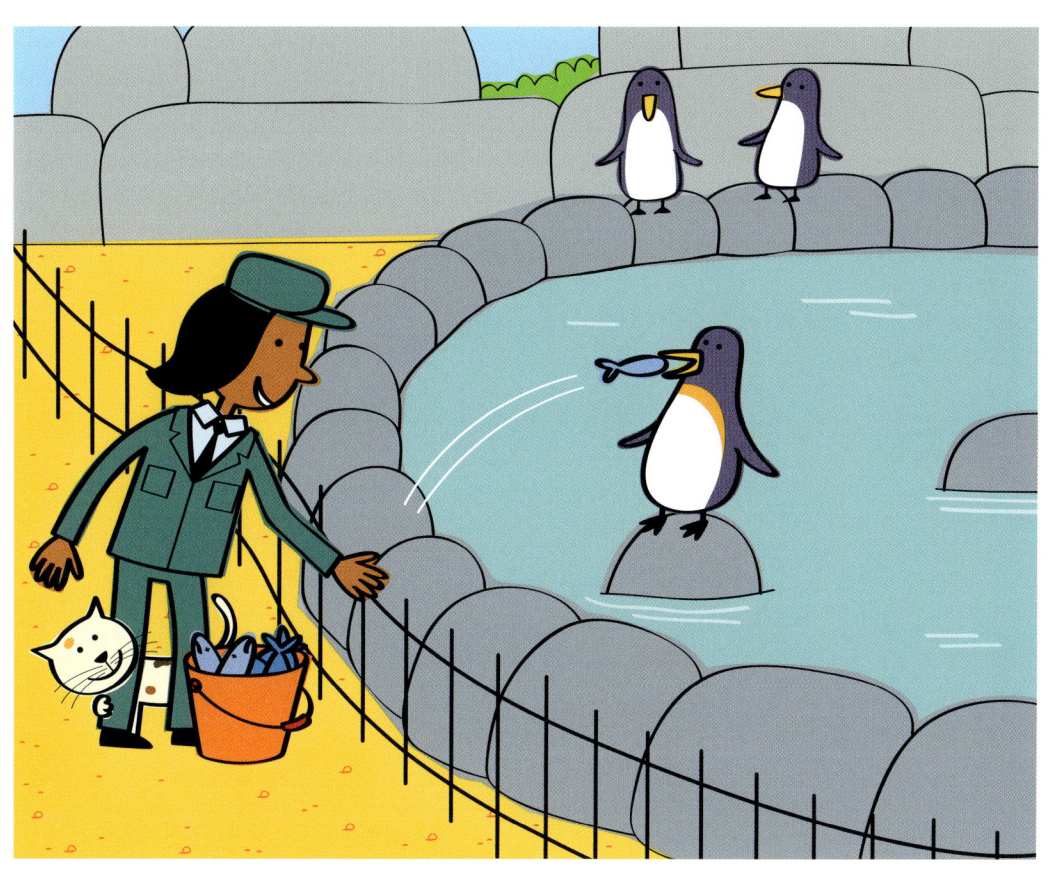

This is for the penguin.

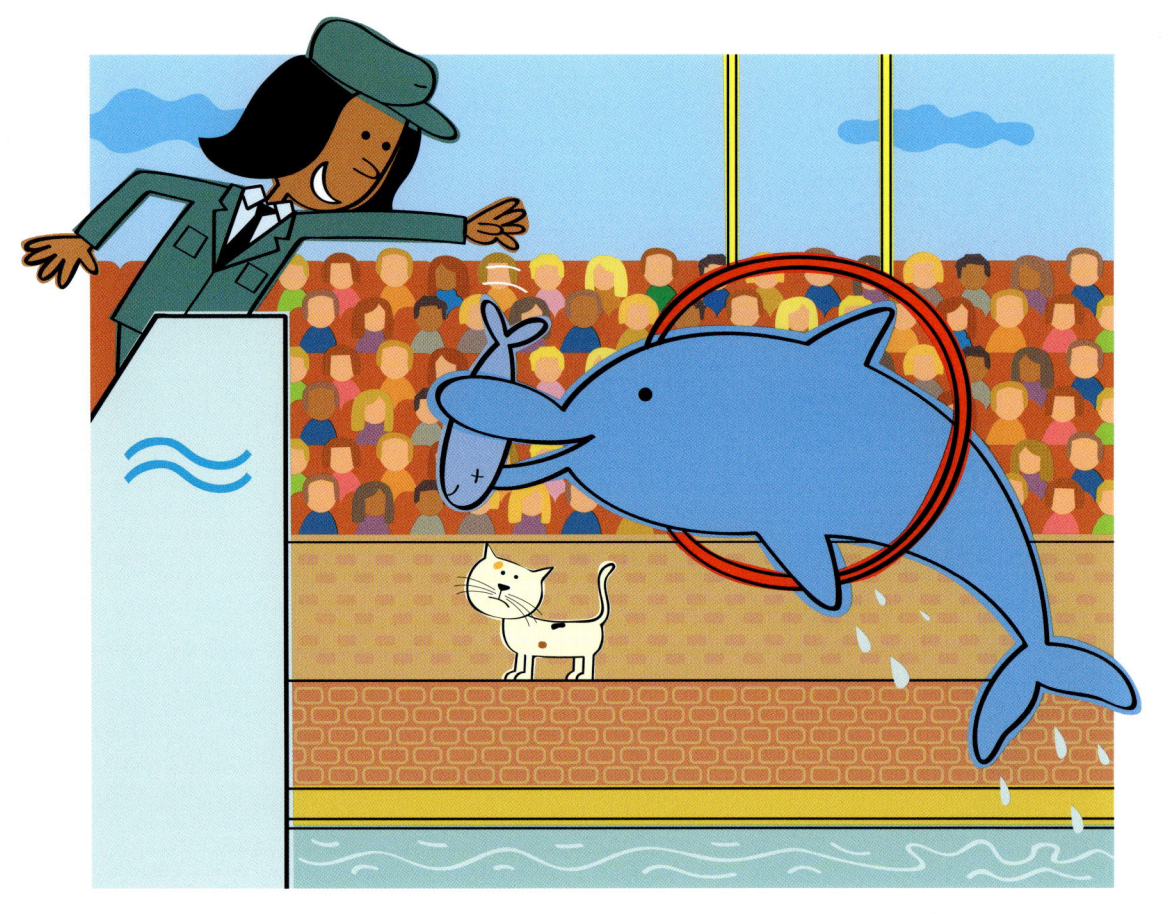

This is for the dolphin.

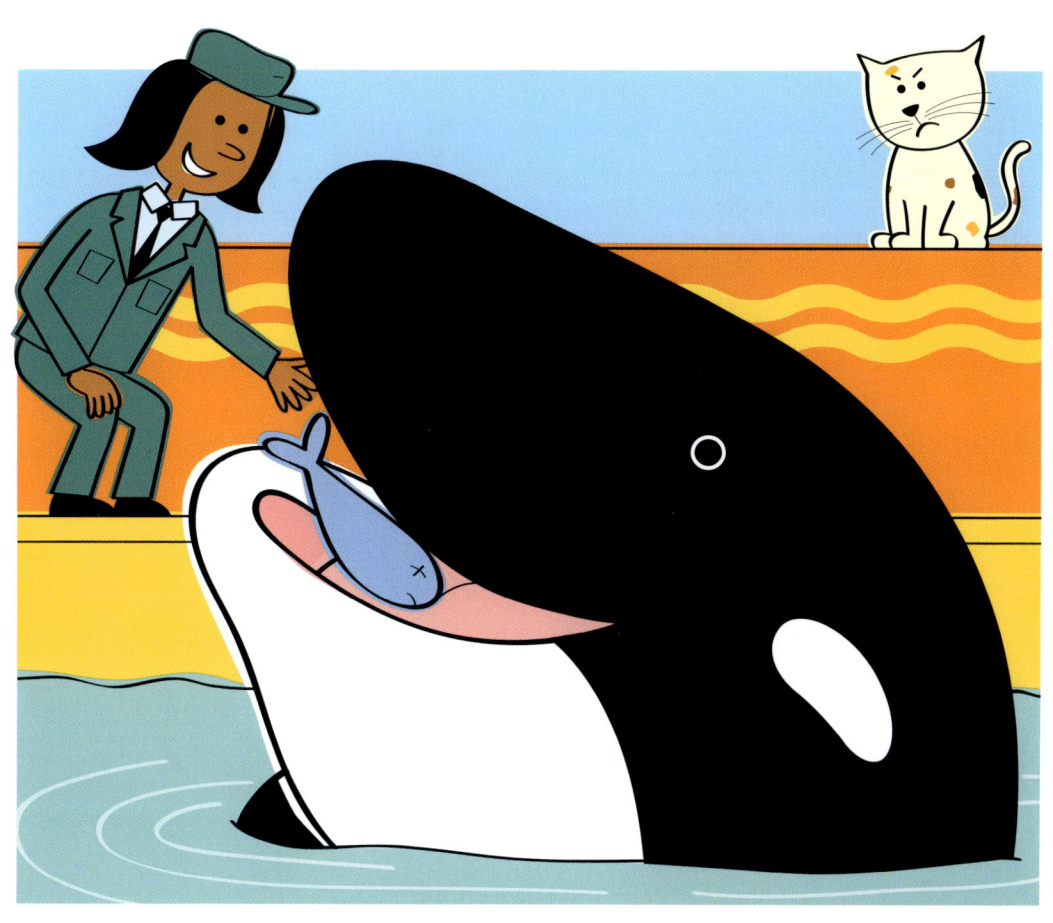

This is for the whale.

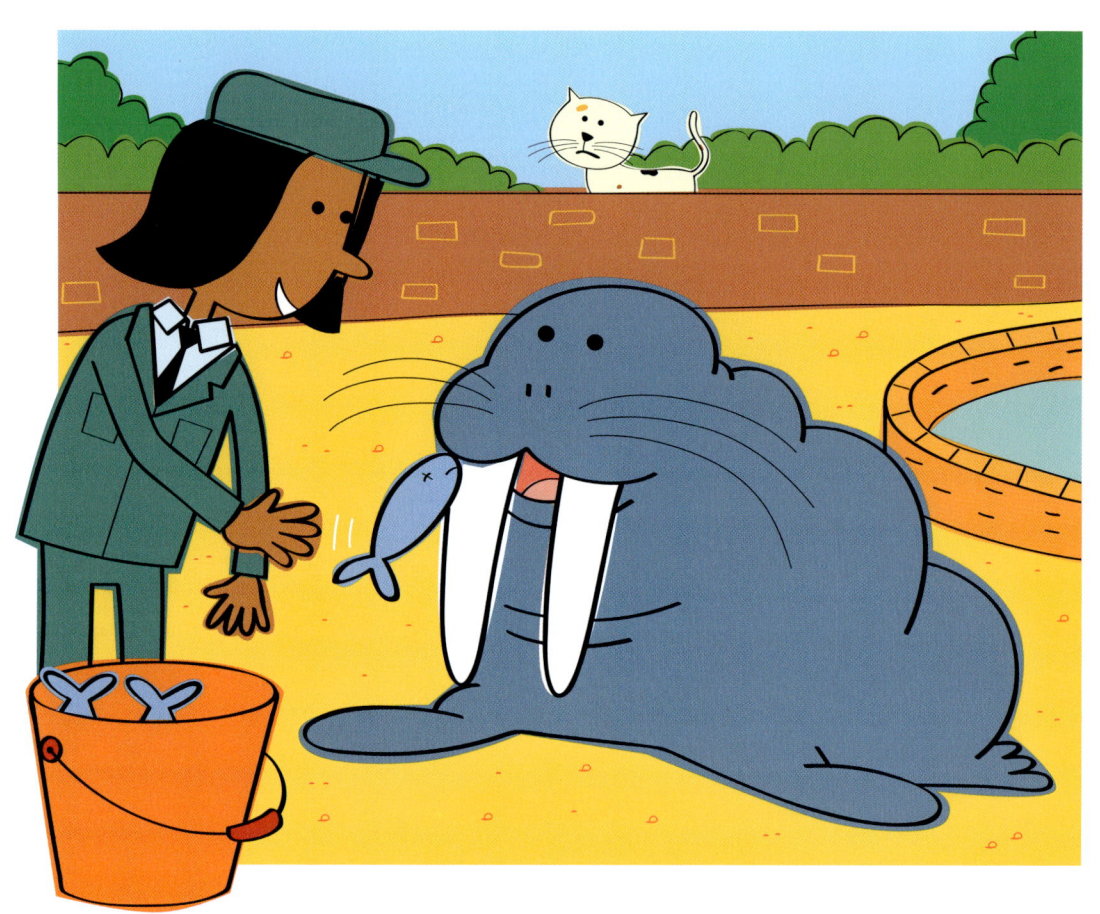

This is for the walrus.

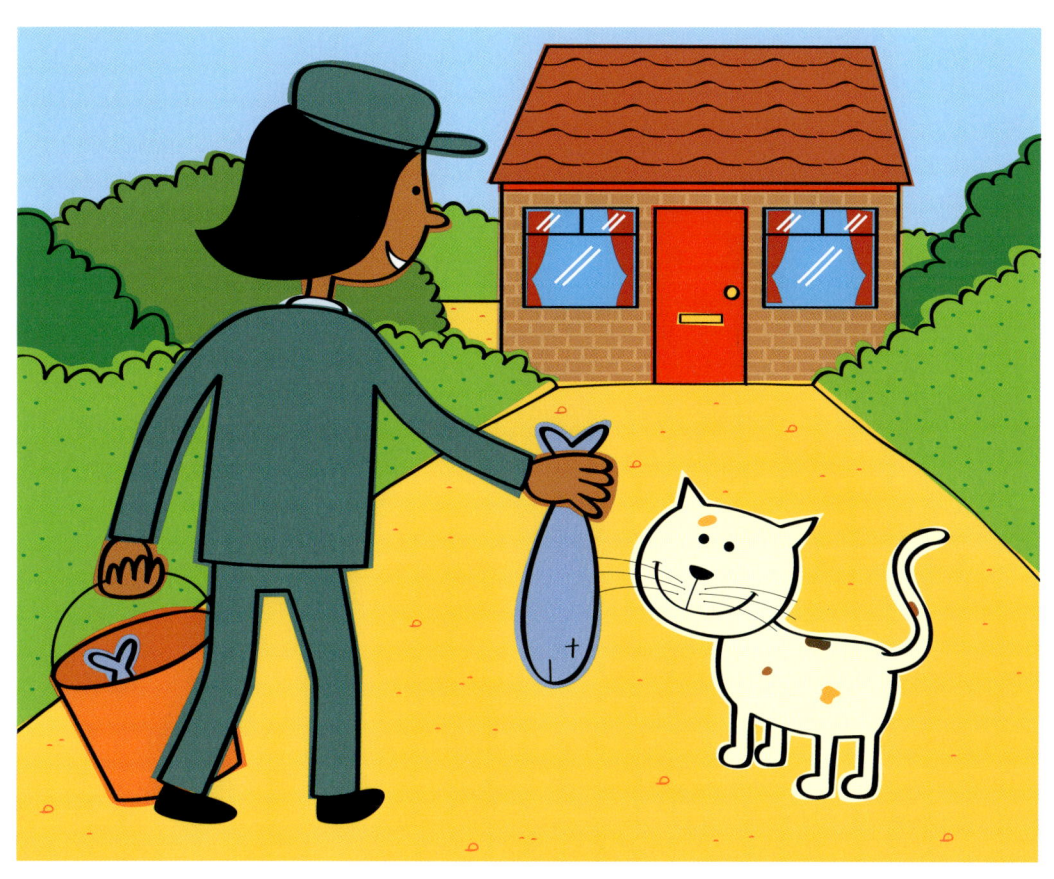

This is for the cat.

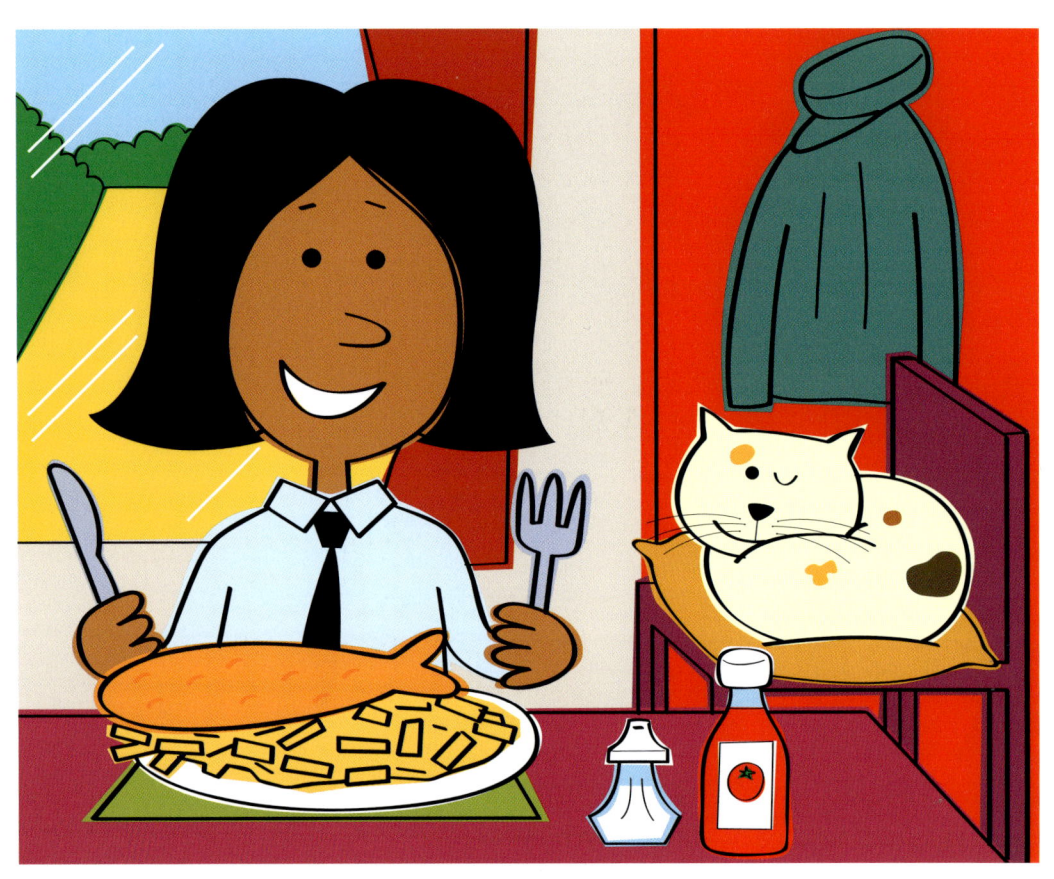

This is for me!